GIFTED & TALENTED®

*To develop
your child's gifts
and talents*

PUZZLES & GAMES

FOR CRITICAL AND CREATIVE THINKING

A Workbook for Ages 6-8

Written by Martha Cheney and Diane Bockwoldt

Illustrated by Larry Nolte

Lowell House
Juvenile

Los Angeles

CONTEMPORARY
BOOKS

Chicago

ISBN 1-56565-139-1

10 9 8 7 6 5

GIFTED & TALENTED® WORKBOOKS will help develop your child's natural talents and gifts by providing activities to enhance critical and creative thinking skills. These skills of logic and reasoning teach children **how** to think. They are precisely the skills emphasized by teachers of gifted and talented children.

Thinking skills are the skills needed to be able to learn anything at any time. Unlike events, words, and teaching methods, thinking skills never change. If a child has a grasp of how to think, school success and even success in life will become more assured. In addition, the child will become self-confident as he or she approaches new tasks with the ability to think them through and discover solutions.

GIFTED & TALENTED® WORKBOOKS present these skills in a unique way, combining the basic subject areas of reading, language arts, and math with thinking skills. The top of each page is labeled to indicate the specific thinking skill developed. Here are some of the skills you will find:

• Deduction — the ability to reach a logical conclusion by interpreting clues

• Understanding Relationships — the ability to recognize how objects, shapes, and words are similar or dissimilar; to classify and categorize

• Sequencing — the ability to organize events, numbers; to recognize patterns

• Inference — the ability to reach logical conclusions from given or assumed evidence

• Creative Thinking — the ability to generate unique ideas; to compare and contrast the same elements in different situations; to present imaginative solutions to problems.

Each book contains activities that challenge children. The activities vary in range from easier to more difficult. You may need to work with your child on many of the pages, especially with the child who is a non-reader. However, even a non-reader can master thinking skills, and the sooner your child learns how to think, the better. Read the directions to your child and, if necessary, explain them. Let your child choose to do the activities that interest him or her. When interest wanes, stop. A page or two at a time may be enough, as the child should have fun while learning.

It is important to remember that these activities are designed to teach your child **how to think**, not how to find the right answer. Teachers of gifted children are never surprised when a child discovers a new "right" answer. For example, a child may be asked to choose the object that doesn't belong in this group: a table, a chair, a book, a desk. The best answer is **book**, since all the others are furniture. But a child could respond that all of them belong because they all could be found in an office or a library. The best way to react to this type of response is to praise the child and gently point out that there is another answer, too. While creativity should be encouraged, your child must look for the best and most **suitable** answer.

GIFTED & TALENTED® WORKBOOKS have been developed and written by teachers. Educationally sound and endorsed by leaders in the gifted field, this series will benefit any child who demonstrates curiosity, imagination, a sense of fun and wonder about the world, and a desire to learn. These books will open your child's mind to new experiences and help fulfill his or her true potential.

Use the letters to fill in the blanks below. Use each letter only once. Read from top to bottom to find the hidden word.

w a o r i n b

○ e d

o r ○ n g e

○ n d i g o

g r e e ○

○ l u e

v i ○ l e t

y e l l o ○

Use the letters to fill in the blanks below. Use each letter only once. Read from top to bottom to find out where the animals live.

a e f h m n o r t

c ◯ w

h e ◯

g o a ◯

◯ o r s e

s h ◯ e p

c a l ◯

c ◯ t

◯ o o s t e r

l a ◯ b

Use all the letters in the alphabet to complete the letter ladder. Use each letter only once.

a b c d e f g h i j k l m n o p q r s t u v w x y z

p i ◯ l o w
p ◯ i n t
h a ◯
◯ u i l t
f u ◯ z y
s n o ◯
i n ◯ h
e i ◯ h t
p a ◯ a m a s
h o r ◯ e
t ◯ b
◯ i n e
h a r ◯ o n i c a
g i ◯ t
c a ◯ d l e
b e ◯
◯ y l o p h o n e
t r u m ◯ e t
v ◯ o l i n
t e l ◯ p h o n e
s ◯ e e p
s n a ◯ e
◯ o p
r a b ◯ i t
b ◯ o k
d ◯ u m

Use all the letters in the alphabet to complete the letter ladder. Use each letter only once.

a b c d e f g h i j k l m n o p q r s t u v w x y z

h a ◯ p y
b ◯ n d
b o ◯
l e ◯ t e r
◯ e l l o w
t i ◯ e r
m o t h ◯ r
b u b ◯ l e
p u ◯ z l e
c ◯ o k i e
p i n ◯
◯ a m
d u ◯ k
◯ i t t l e
f l o ◯ e r
◯ u e e n
w ◯ n d o w
◯ i n g e r
b i r t h ◯ a y
n u ◯ b e r
s q u a ◯ e
s e ◯ e n
◯ t o p
f r i e ◯ d
f ◯ n n y
o t ◯ e r

What's wrong with this picture? Find the parts of the picture that **don't** make sense. Circle them.

Lots of things are wrong with this picture! Find the parts of the picture that **do** make sense. Circle them.

What's wrong with this picture? Find the parts of the picture that **don't** make sense. Circle them.

Hidden in this outer space scene are pictures of foods we eat and drink. Circle all the foods you can find. Write the number below.

How many foods did you find? _____

Hidden in the flower garden are pictures of things that people wear. Circle as many as you can find.

How many did you find? _____

Find 15 schoolroom items hidden in and around this "school" of fish.

On the lines below, write the name of each item you find.

_____ _____ _____

_____ _____ _____

_____ _____ _____

_____ _____ _____

_____ _____ _____

What is in the bag? Draw a picture of your idea in the box below.

What is in the crate? Draw a picture of your idea in the box below.

What is in the truck? Is the delivery for the fire station, the store, or the school? Draw a picture of your idea in the box below.

What is caught on the fisherman's line? Draw a picture of your idea in the box below.

Complete the picture by drawing the missing half of the monster.

Complete the picture by drawing the missing half of the troll.

Complete the picture by drawing the missing half of the fairy and then the frog.

On the lines below, write a story about a fairy, a monster, a troll, and a frog. Use additional paper if you need to.

_____

_____

_____

_____

_____

_____

_____

_____

Circle the answer that makes the **most** sense. The first one has been done for you.

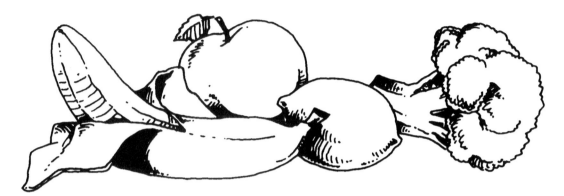

Yellow is to banana as red is to	apple	pencil
Sour is to lemon as sweet is to	broccoli	candy
Fur is to bear as feather is to	bird	jacket
Hard is to rock as soft is to	ice cube	pillow
Moon is to night as sun is to	day	island
Pool is to swim as bed is to	sleep	read
Chair is to sit as bike is to	push	ride

Circle the answer that makes the **most** sense.

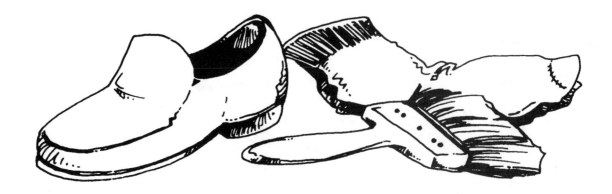

Foot is to shoe as hand is to	sock	glove
Fish is to swim as bird is to	fly	float
Kitten is to cat as puppy is to	bear	dog
Over is to under as high is to	up	low
Friday is to day as January is to	February	month
Pen is to ink as brush is to	paint	write
Eye is to see as ear is to	speak	hear

Circle the answer that makes the **most** sense.

Oak is to tree as poodle is to	pig	dog
String is to guitar as key is to	lock	piano
Bottom is to top as hot is to	water	cold
Pencil is to write as candle is to	burn	draw
Plane is to sky as car is to	road	drive
Kangaroo is to hop as snake is to	bounce	slither
Bark is to dog as quack is to	duck	bird

See how many words you can find in the grid below. Words may be formed by using any letter squares that touch each other horizontally, vertically, or diagonally. Each letter square may be used only once in each word.

T	S	I	P
A	D	O	L
Y	H	T	A
O	E	R	E

On the lines below, list the words you find. The first one has been done for you.

hop _____   _____

_____   _____

_____   _____

_____

_____

_____

See how many words you can find in the grid below. Words may be formed by using any letter squares that touch each other horizontally, vertically, or diagonally. Each letter square may be used only once in each word.

C	H	L	E
O	B	S	V
B	U	O	T
M	D	F	A

On the lines below, list the words you find.

See how many words you can find in the grid below. Words may be formed by using any letter squares that touch each other horizontally, vertically, or diagonally. Each letter square may be used only once in each word.

B	L	L	Y
A	I	A	C
N	F	M	E
K	U	E	S

On the lines below, list the words you find.

_____   _____

_____   _____

_____   _____

_____   _____

_____   _____

_____   _____

See how many words you can find in the grid below. Words may be formed by using any letter squares that touch each other horizontally, vertically, or diagonally. Each letter square may be used only once in each word.

L	B	I	R
O	G	C	L
I	A	E	K
L	T	X	N

On the lines below, list the words you find.

_____   _____

_____   _____

_____   _____

_____   _____

_____

_____

_____

Use the squiggle line to draw a picture in the frame. Write a story to go with your picture on the lines below it. Use additional paper if you need to.

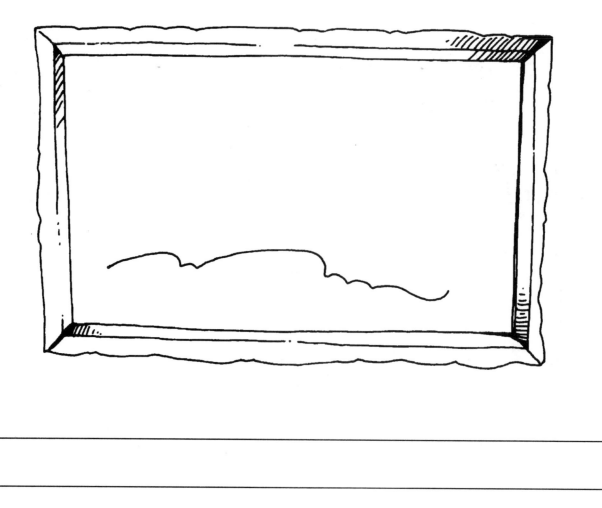

Use the squiggle line to draw a picture in the window. Write a story to go with your picture on the lines below it. Use additional paper if you need to.

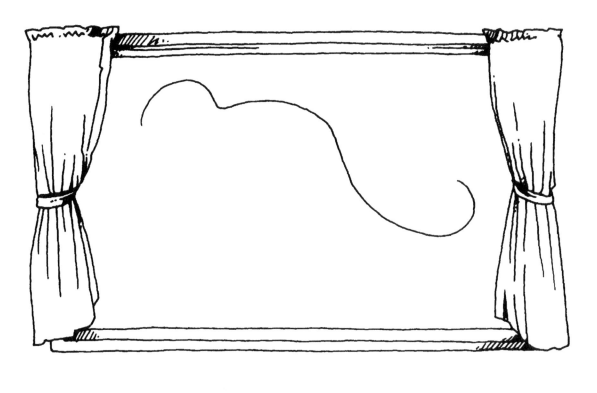

_____

_____

_____

_____

_____

_____

Use the squiggle line to draw a picture in the frame. Write a story to go with your picture on the lines below it. Use additional paper if you need to.

_____

_____

_____

_____

_____

_____

_____

Use the squiggle line to draw a map. Write a story to go with your map on the lines below it. Use additional paper if you need to.

_____

_____

_____

_____

_____

_____

_____

Number the pictures in order so that they tell a story.
Draw a picture of your own in the empty box to show what
happens next.

___

___

___

4

Number the pictures in order so that they tell a story.
Draw a picture of your own in the empty box to show what
happens next.

———

———

———

4

Number the pictures in order so that they tell a story.
Draw a picture of your own in the empty box to show what
happens first.

1

Number the pictures in order so that they tell a story.
Draw a picture of your own in the empty box to show what happens first.

1

These are bezzuzziks.

These are **not** bezzuzziks.

Circle the bezzuzziks in this row.

Draw three bezzuzziks of your own in the box below.

How can you recognize a bezzuzzik? Write your answer on the lines.

These are dodoloos.

These are **not** dodoloos.

Circle the dodoloos in this row.

Draw three dodoloos of your own in the box below.

How can you recognize a dodoloo? Write your answer on the lines.

These are perkles.

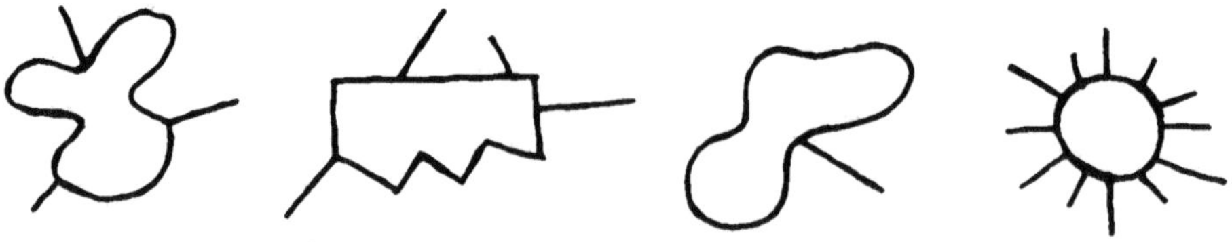

These are **not** perkles.

Circle the perkles in this row.

Draw three perkles of your own in the box below.

How can you recognize a perkle? Write your answer on the lines.

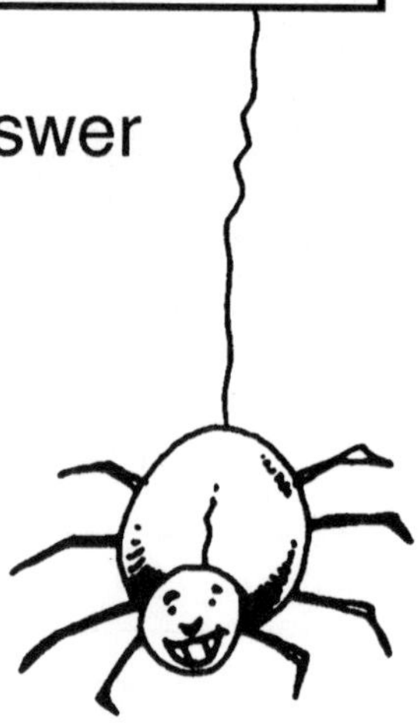

_____

_____

_____

_____

Use the clues to figure out which boy is which. Write each boy's name on the line nearest him.

Freddy only eats things that are shaped like circles.
Eddy only eats things that come in pairs.
Teddy likes sandwiches.

Use the clues to find out who lives in each apartment. Write your answers on the lines below.

Mrs. Pinky lives in Apartment 2.
Mr. Smith does not live next door to Mr. Jones.
Ms. Becker does not live in Apartment 4.
Mr. Jones lives next door to Mrs. Pinky.

Apartment 1: _____

Apartment 2: _Mrs. Pinky_____

Apartment 3: _____

Apartment 4: _____

Maria, Kim, and Allison are sisters. Use the clues to find out which girl is which. Write their names on the lines below them.

Maria is not the shortest sister.
Allison is not the first in line.
Kim is shorter than Allison.

_____   _____   _____

What comes next in each pattern? Draw your answers on the lines.

Continue each pattern. Draw your answers on the lines.

○□○○□□○□ ___ ___ ___

□□○○○□□○○□ ___ ___ ___

△○○|△○○|△ ___ ___ ___

Continue each pattern. Draw your answers on the lines.

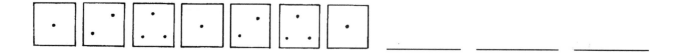

_____ _____ _____

_____ _____ _____

_____ _____ _____

Draw some more items that belong in this group.

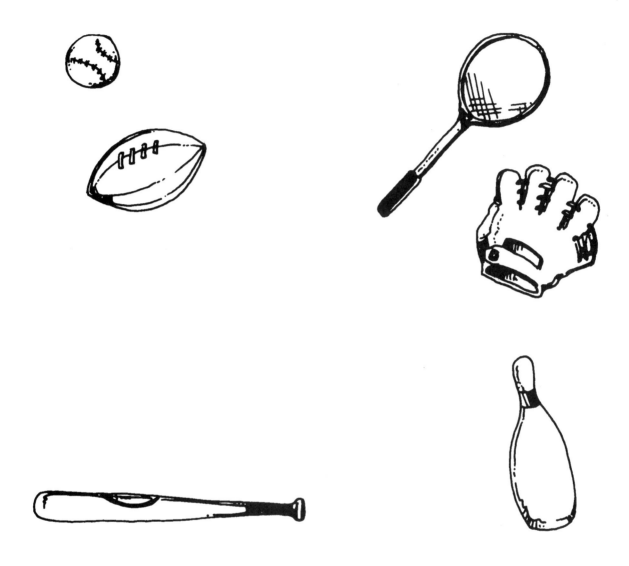

Why do these items belong together? Write your answer on the lines.

_____

_____

_____

Draw some more items that belong in this group.

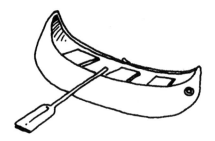

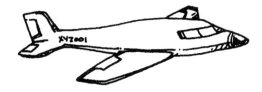

Why do these items belong together? Write your answer on the lines.

_____

_____

_____

These are woozles.

These are **not** woozles.

Circle the woozles in this row.

Draw three woozles of your own in the box below.

How can you recognize a woozle? Write your answer
on the lines.

These are smileks.

These are **not** smileks.

Circle the smileks in this row.

Draw three smileks of your own in the box below.

How can you recognize a smilek? Write your answer on the lines.

What comes next in each pattern? Circle the correct object.

In the space below, draw a pattern of your own. Ask a friend to circle the correct answer.

What comes next in each pattern? Fill in the blanks.

c   f   i   l   o   r   ___ ___ ___

1 2 4 8 16 32 ___ ___ ___

28 26 24 22 20 ___ ___ ___

a z b y c x d ___ ___ ___

85 81 77 73 69 ___ ___ ___

What comes next in each pattern? Fill in the blanks.

3 6 9 12 15 ___ ___ ___

5 10 15 20 25 ___ ___ ___

z y x w v u ___ ___ ___

a 1 b 2 c 3 ___ ___ ___

6 12 18 24 30 ___ ___ ___

What comes next in each pattern? Circle the correct answer.

aa ab ac ad ae   ag af

1 1 1 2 1 3 1 4 1 5 1   1 6

2   4   6   8   10   11 12

f   h   j   l   n   q p

42 38 34 30 26   22 24

In the box below, draw a picture of something you could make using these items:

Write a sentence about your creation.

_____

_____

_____

In the box below, draw a picture of something you could make using these items:

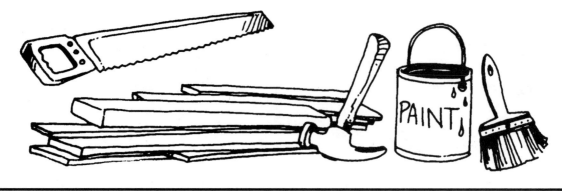

Write a sentence about your creation.

_____

_____

_____

In the box below, draw a picture of something you could make using these items:

Write a sentence about your creation.

_____

_____

_____

Draw some more items that belong in this group.

Why do these items belong together? Write your answer on the lines.

_____

_____

_____

Draw some more items that belong in this group.

Why do these items belong together? Write your answer on the lines.

_____

_____

_____

Draw some more items that belong in this group.

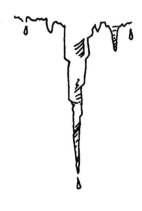

Why do these items belong together? Write your answer on the lines.

_____

_____

_____

Look at the picture. On the lines below, write what the child is thinking.

_____

_____

_____

_____

_____

Look at the picture. On the lines below, write what each character is thinking.

Painter: _____

_____

Lady: _____

_____

Dog: _____

_____

Look at the picture. On the lines below, write what each child is thinking.

Boy: _____

_____

_____

Girl: _____

_____

_____

Be a chef. Create a recipe using these ingredients:

orange juice
peanut butter
flour
onion
hot dogs

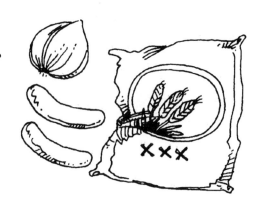

Draw a picture of your creation in the box. On the lines below, describe how you made it.

Create a make-believe creature using parts of the animals below. Draw your creature in the box. On the lines below, write some information about your creature. Give it a name.

_____

_____

_____

_____

_____

Be an inventor. Create a contraption using the items below. Draw a picture of your contraption in the box. On the lines below, give it a name and describe what it is used for.

_____

_____

_____

_____

_____

Look at the group of words listed below. Why do they belong together? Try to add more words to the list.

gate
door
mouth
book

_____

_____

_____

_____

Write a sentence explaining how all of these words relate to each other.

_____

_____

_____

Look at the group of words listed below. Why do they belong together? Try to add more words to the list.

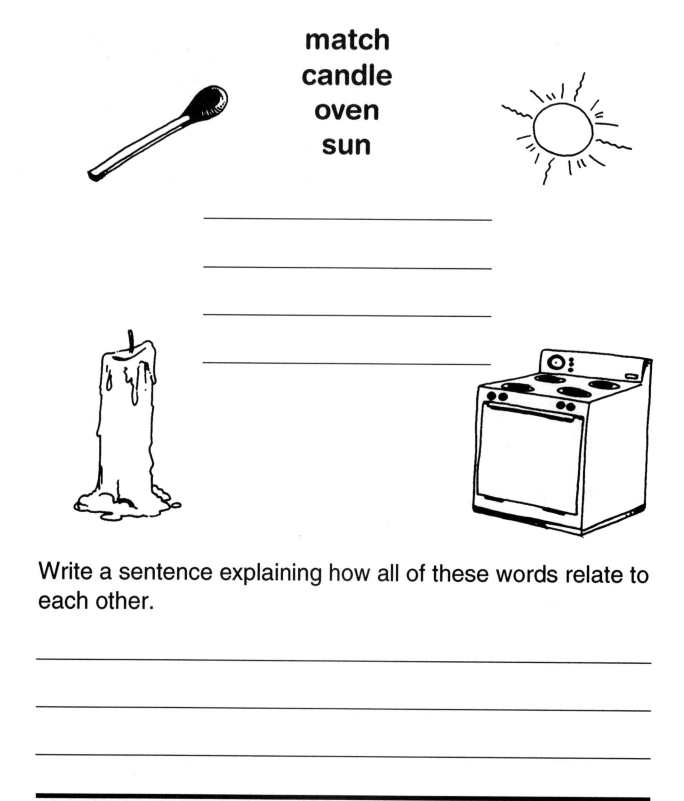

match
candle
oven
sun

_____

_____

_____

_____

Write a sentence explaining how all of these words relate to each other.

_____

_____

_____

Look at the group of words listed below. Why do they belong together? Try to add more words to the list.

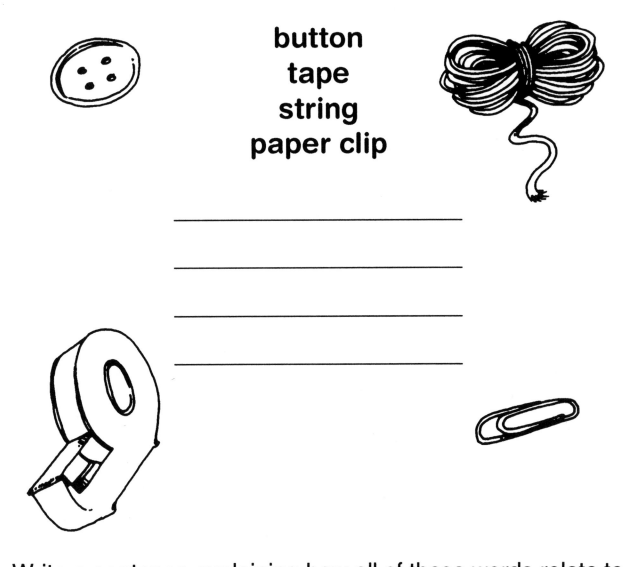

button
tape
string
paper clip

_____

_____

_____

_____

Write a sentence explaining how all of these words relate to each other.

_____

_____

_____

Connect the dots to find a message from the teacher. Write the message on the lines below.

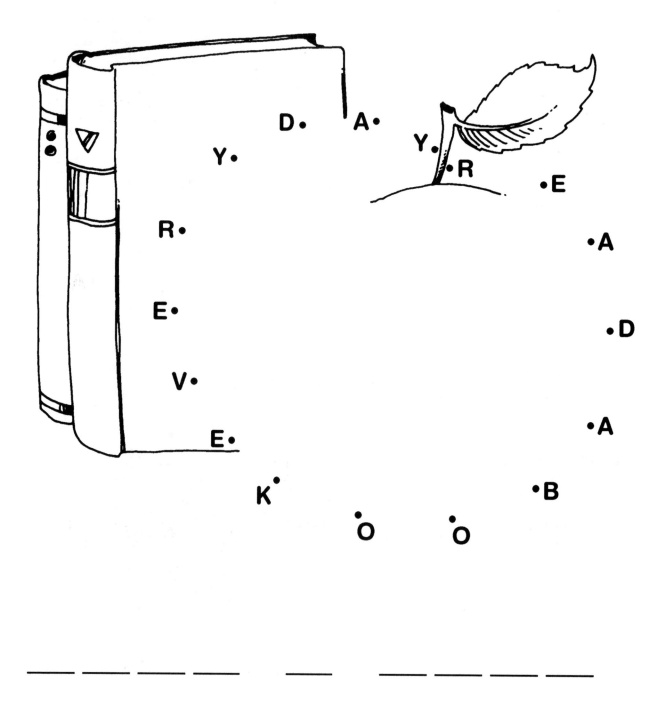

_ _ _ _ _ _ _ _ _ _ _ _ _

_ _ _ _ _ _ _ _ _ _ _ .

Connect the dots to find a message from the animals. Write the message on the lines below.

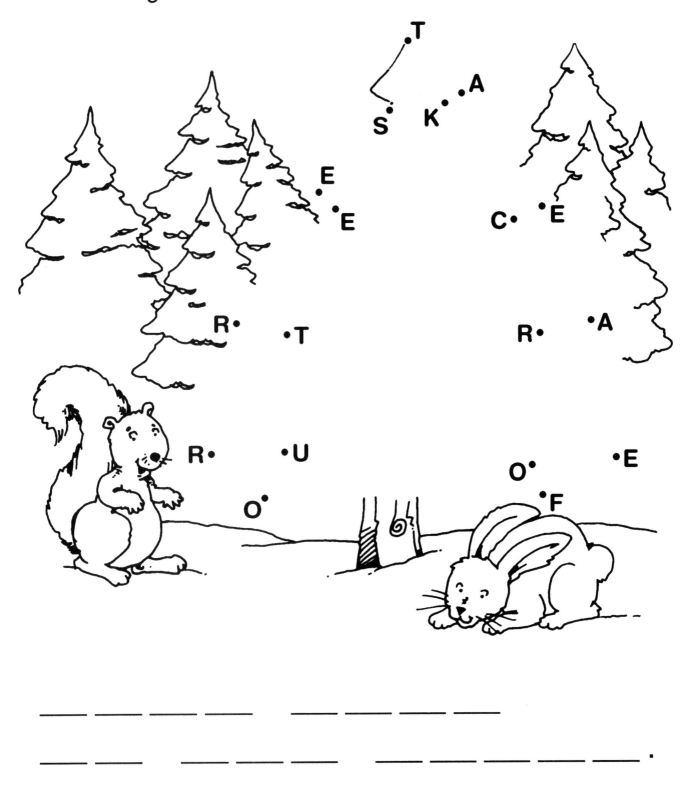

_____ _____ _____ _____   _____ _____ _____

_____ _____   _____ _____ _____   _____ _____ _____ .

Follow the dots in alphabetical order to find a hidden picture.

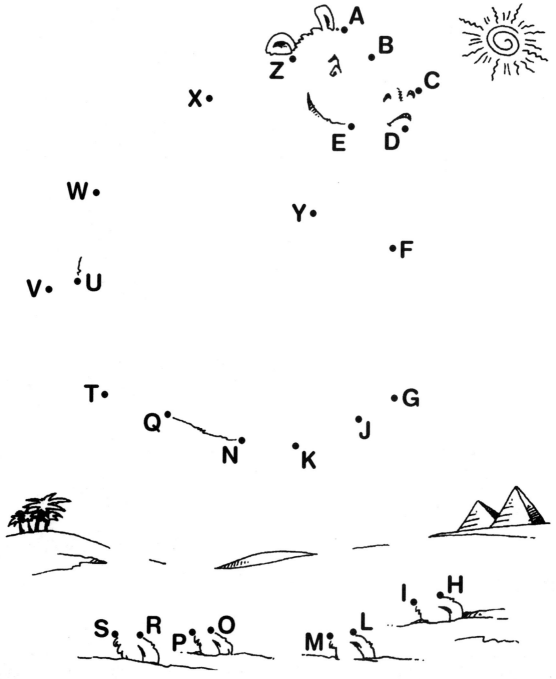

On another piece of paper, make your own dot-to-dot puzzle. Use all the letters of the alphabet. You can ask a friend to solve the puzzle.

Use the code to find the secret message.

1	**2**	**3**	**4**	**5**	**6**	**7**	**8**	**9**	**10**
a	b	c	d	e	f	g	h	i	j

11	**12**	**13**	**14**	**15**	**16**	**17**	**18**	**19**	**20**
k	l	m	n	o	p	q	r	s	t

21	**22**	**23**	**24**	**25**	**26**
u	v	w	x	y	z

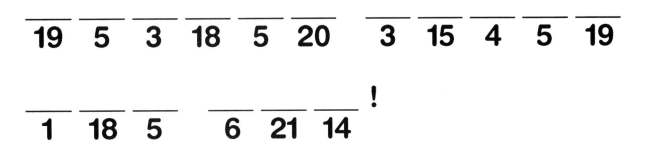

Write the message on the lines.

__	__	__	__	__	__		__	__	__	__	__
19	**5**	**3**	**18**	**5**	**20**		**3**	**15**	**4**	**5**	**19**

__	__	__		__	__	__	!
1	**18**	**5**		**6**	**21**	**14**	

Use the code to find the secret message.

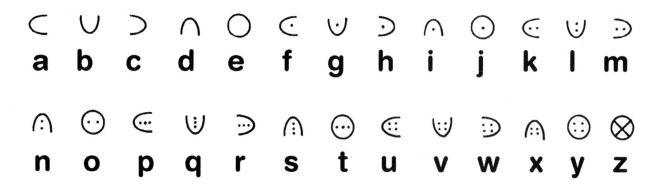

Write the message on the lines.

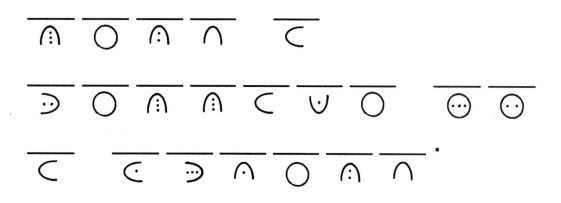

See how many words you can find in the grid below. Words may be formed by using any letter squares that touch each other horizontally, vertically, or diagonally. Each letter square may be used only once in each word.

D	E	Y	K
E	S	S	E
R	H	C	R
L	O	O	T

On the lines below, list the words you find.

_____   _____

_____   _____

_____   _____

_____   _____

_____   _____

_____   _____

See how many words you can find in the grid below. Words may be formed by using any letter squares that touch each other horizontally, vertically, or diagonally. Each letter square may be used only once in each word.

R	E	P	E
E	D	I	T
H	A	R	Y
S	F	L	G

On the lines below, list the words you find.

_____   _____

_____   _____

_____   _____

_____   _____

_____   _____

_____   _____

_____   _____

Page 5:
rainbow

Page 6:
on the farm

Page 7:
pillow, paint, hay, quilt, fuzzy, snow, inch, eight, pajamas, horse, tub, vine, harmonica, gift, candle, bed, xylophone, trumpet, violin, telephone, sheep, snake, top, rabbit, book, drum

Page 8:
happy, band, box, letter, yellow, tiger, mother, bubble, puzzle, cookie, pink, jam, duck, little, flower, queen, window, finger, birthday, number, square, seven, stop, friend, funny, other

Page 9:

Page 10:

Page 11:

Page 12:

How many foods did you find? **15**

Page 13:

How many did you find? **11**

Page 14:

On the lines below, write the name of each item you find.

pencil	note book	globe
crayon	paint brush	apple
book	scissors	lunchbox
desk	flag	map
eraser	computer	bell

Pages 15-22:
Answers will vary.

Page 23:

Yellow is to banana as red is to — (apple), pencil
Sour is to lemon as sweet is to — broccoli, (candy)
Fur is to bear as feather is to — (bird), jacket
Hard is to rock as soft is to — ice cube, (pillow)
Moon is to night as sun is to — (day), island
Pool is to swim as bed is to — (sleep), read
Chair is to sit as bike is to — push, (ride)

Page 24:

Foot is to shoe as hand is to — sock, (glove)
Fish is to swim as bird is to — (fly), float
Kitten is to cat as puppy is to — bear, (dog)
Over is to under as high is to — up, (low)
Friday is to day as January is to — February, (month)
Pen is to ink as brush is to — (paint), write
Eye is to see as ear is to — speak, (hear)

Page 25:

Oak is to tree as poodle is to — pig, (dog)
String is to guitar as key is to — lock, (piano)
Bottom is to top as hot is to — water, (cold)
Pencil is to write as candle is to — (burn), draw
Plane is to sky as car is to — (road), drive
Kangaroo is to hop as snake is to — bounce, (slither)
Bark is to dog as quack is to — (duck), bird

Page 26:
Answers will vary. Some of the words are: SIP, STAY, DAY, HERE, EAT.

Page 27:
Answers will vary. Some of the words are: SOFA, FUSE, BUS, MUD, USE.

Page 28:
Answers will vary. Some of the words are: MAIL, YAM, FUME, CLAY, LINK.

Page 29:
Answers will vary. Some of the words are: BOAT, AXE, NECK, GOAT, RIB.

Pages 30-33:
Answers will vary.

Page 34:

Page 35:

Page 36:

Page 37:

Page 38:

A bezzuzzik is an object that is equal on both sides, with the right side colored in.

Page 39:

A dodoloo is an object that is closed all the way around.

Page 40:

A perkle is an object that is closed all the way around and has lines, or rays, coming out of it.

Page 41:

Teddy   Freddy   Eddy

Page 42:
Apartment 1: Mr. Jones
Apartment 2: Mrs. Pinky
Apartment 3: Ms. Becker
Apartment 4: Mr. Smith

Page 43:

Maria   Allison   Kim

Page 44:

Page 45:

Page 46:

Page 47:
All the items are used to play sports.

Page 48:
All the items are vehicles that can carry people from place to place.

Page 49:

A woozle has curved lines, no straight lines.

Page 50:

A smilek has lines that cross over each other, or intersect, and two dots.

Page 51:

Page 52:

c f i l o r <u>u</u> <u>X</u>

1 2 4 8 16 32 <u>64</u> <u>128</u> <u>256</u>

28 26 24 22 20 <u>18</u> <u>16</u> <u>14</u>

a z b y c x d <u>w</u> <u>e</u> <u>v</u>

85 81 77 73 69 <u>65</u> <u>61</u> <u>57</u>

Page 53:

3 6 9 12 15 <u>18</u> <u>21</u> <u>24</u>

5 10 15 20 25 <u>30</u> <u>35</u> <u>40</u>

z y x w v u <u>t</u> <u>s</u> <u>r</u>

a 1 b 2 c 3 <u>d</u> <u>4</u> <u>e</u>

6 12 18 24 30 <u>36</u> <u>42</u> <u>48</u>

Page 54:

aa ab ac ad ae   ag (af)

1 1 1 2 1 3 1 4 1 5 1   1 (6)

2 4 6 8 10   11 (12)

f h j l n   q (p)

42 38 34 30 26   (22) 24

Pages 55-57:
Answers will vary.

Page 58:
All of them can be found on a farm.

Page 59:
All of them are foods that begin with P.

Page 60:
All of them can melt.

Pages 61-66:
Answers will vary.

Page 67:
All of them are objects that can be opened and closed.

Page 68:
All of them are objects that can give off heat.

Page 69:
All of them are objects that can fasten things together.

Page 70:
Read a book every day.

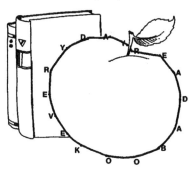

Page 71:
Take care of our trees.

Page 72:

Page 73:
Secret codes are fun!

Page 74:
Send a message to a friend.

Page 75:
Answers will vary. Some of the words are: YES, KEYS, TOOL, SEED, DESK.

Page 76:
Answers will vary. Some of the words are: SAID, READ, TRIP, FADE, DIP.